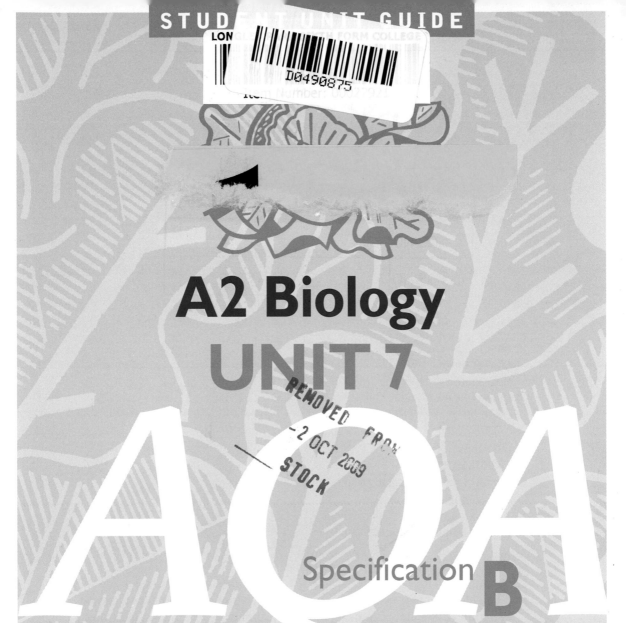

A2 Biology
UNIT 7

AQA
Specification B

Module 7: Microbes and Disease

Keith Hirst

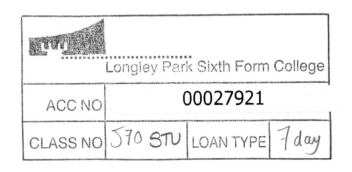

Philip Allan Updates
Market Place
Deddington
Oxfordshire
OX15 0SE

tel: 01869 338652
fax: 01869 337590
e-mail: sales@philipallan.co.uk
www.philipallan.co.uk

© Philip Allan Updates 2002

ISBN 0 86003 478 X

This Guide has been written specifically to support students preparing for the AQA Specification B A2 Biology Unit 7 examination. The content has been neither approved nor endorsed by AQA and remains the sole responsibility of the author.

Printed by Information Press, Eynsham, Oxford

Contents

Introduction

■ ■ ■

Content Guidance

■ ■ ■

Questions and Answers

Introduction

About this guide

This guide is for students following the AQA Specification B A2 Biology course. It deals with Unit 7, which examines the content of **Module 7: Microbes and Disease**. The key to success is examination technique. You should always have at the back of your mind the type of questions that can be asked, when both learning and revising a topic. This Introduction is devoted to the aims of the specification and to learning and revision skills. The Content Guidance section provides an outline of the topics you need to know and understand and includes detailed explanations of some of the topics. The Question and Answer section contains sample unit test questions, together with candidate responses which are accompanied by examiner's comments.

The best way to use this book is to:
- revise a topic using the Content Guidance section as a guide
- attempt the relevant question(s) *without looking* at the candidate responses
- compare your responses with the candidate responses and examiner's comments and see what marks you might have achieved
- revise the parts of the topic for which you did not obtain high marks

The aims of the A2 specification

A2 biology encourages you to:
- develop knowledge and understanding of concepts of biology
- develop the skills to use this knowledge and understanding in new situations
- develop an understanding of the methods used by scientists
- be aware of advances in technology that are relevant to biology
- recognise the value and responsible use of biology in society
- sustain and develop an interest in, and enjoyment of, biology
- show knowledge and understanding of the facts, principles and concepts from different areas of biology and to make and use connections between them

How the unit test assesses these aims

Very few marks in the unit test are given for simple recall of knowledge. Most of the marks are given for being able to:
- demonstrate understanding of concepts
- apply knowledge and understanding

These two areas include many skills, most or all of which will be addressed later in the unit test. In summary, you should be able to do the following:

- Draw on your knowledge to show understanding of the ethical, social, economic, environmental and technological implications and applications of biology. Read scientific articles in newspapers and periodicals, and watch documentaries on current affairs that deal with scientific issues so that you are aware of different viewpoints on controversial issues.
- Select, organise and present relevant information clearly and logically.
- Practise answering the longer section B questions that require continuous prose.
- Describe, explain and interpret phenomena and effects in terms of biological principles and concepts, presenting arguments and ideas clearly and logically. Make sure you know the difference between the 'trigger' words *explain* and *describe.*
- Interpret (and translate from one form into another) data presented as continuous prose, or in tables, diagrams, drawings and graphs. You will be presented with data in many different forms in the unit test. Make sure that you have practised questions involving comprehension, graphs, tables and diagrams.
- Apply biological principles and concepts in solving problems in unfamiliar situations, including those relating to the ethical, social, economic and technological implications and applications of biology. There will always be unfamiliar data in the unit test and the examiner will ask you to 'suggest' explanations. Again, make sure that you have practised many examples of this type of question.
- Assess the validity of biological information, experiments, inferences and statements. Don't leave your experimental skills in the laboratory. Questions that involve interpreting and evaluating data will usually appear in the unit tests.

A unit test will require the use of most, if not all, of these skills.

In addition, the unit will test your ability to:
- bring together principles and concepts from different areas of biology and apply them in particular contexts
- use biological knowledge in contexts which bring together different areas of the subject.

These are known as synoptic skills. Questions on these skills will be flagged by the icon **S**.

Weightings

Section A of Unit 7 carries *10% of the total A-level mark.* Of this 10%:
- 3.5% of the marks are given for demonstrating knowledge and understanding of the unit content
- 2.5% of the marks are given for being able to apply this knowledge and understanding in new situations
- 4% of the marks are given for demonstrating synoptic knowledge, understanding and skills derived from Modules 1–5.

Section B of the unit test carries *10% of the total A-level mark*. This 10% is entirely synoptic, comprising data-handling questions and a choice of one from two essay questions.

Command terms

Examiners use *trigger words* to advise you which skill they are testing. You must know what the examiner wants when these trigger words appear in a question.

Name/what is the name of...?

This usually requires a technical term or its equivalent. Answers to this type of question normally involve no more than one or two words. Do not waste time by repeating the question in the answer.

List...

This requires you to give a number of features or points, each often no more than a single word, so do not go into further detail.

Define/what is meant by...?

'Define' requires a statement giving the meaning of a particular term or word. 'What is meant by...?' is used frequently in questions on a comprehension passage. It emphasises that a formal definition as such is not required.

Outline...

This means give a brief summary of the main points. There are two good indications as to the amount of detail required. These are the mark allocations and the space allowed for the answer — usually two lines per mark.

Describe...

This means no more than it says: 'Give a description of...'. So 'Describe a curve on a graph' requires a description of the shape of the curve, preferably related to key points or values; 'Describe an experiment' means give an account of how such an experiment might be carried out.

Describe how you...

The emphasis here is on the word *you* and the expression is often used when asking questions about experimental design. What is required is an account of how something could be done by you as a student working in an ordinary school or college laboratory.

Evaluate...

Evaluating is more than just listing advantages and disadvantages. It requires an explanation. Evaluating the evidence for and against a particular point of view requires an explanation of each of the points being made.

Explain...

This requires you to give a reason or interpretation, not a description. The term 'describe' answers the question 'what?' The term 'explain' answers the question 'why?' Thus, 'Explain a curve on a graph' requires a biological reason for any change of direction or pattern that is evident.

Suggest...

Suggest is used when it is not possible to give the answer directly from the facts you have learned. The answer should be based on your general understanding of biology rather than on recall of learnt material. It also indicates that there may be a number of correct alternatives.

Give the evidence for.../using examples from...

Answers to questions involving these phrases must follow the instructions. Marks are *only* awarded for appropriate references to the information provided in the question.

Plot/sketch...

These terms refer to the drawing of graphs. 'Plot' means that the data should be presented as an appropriate graph on graph paper with the points plotted accurately. 'Sketch' requires a simple estimate of the expected curve, and can be made on ordinary lined paper. However, even in a sketched graph, the axes should be correctly labelled.

Calculate...

This term is used where the only requirement is a numerical answer expressed in appropriate units. The additional instruction, 'Show your working', will be used if details or methods are required. Make sure that you can calculate percentages and proportions, since these appear in most unit tests.

The unit test

Unit Test 7 is different from previous unit tests (apart from Unit Test 5) in that as well as questions on the content of Module 7, it contains questions testing *understanding of principles from earlier modules*. It may also contain questions testing *experimental and investigative skills*. The specification states that candidates should be able to:

- bring together principles and concepts from different areas of biology and apply them in a particular context clearly and logically and using appropriate specialist vocabulary
- use biological skills in contexts which bring together different areas of biology

Synoptic testing is very important, since it accounts for 40% of the total marks available in the A2 course.

Unit 7

Time allowed: 2 hours 15 minutes

Section A, which tests the content of Module 7, is worth 50 marks. It contains both short, structured questions and longer questions requiring extended writing. Of the 50 marks, approximately 20 are synoptic, involving principles from Modules 1, 2, 3, 4, 5 and AO3 skills in the context of microbes and disease. The synoptic parts of questions are indicated by an **S** in the margin next to the question. It is recommended that you spend 60 minutes on Section A questions.

Section B is entirely synoptic and is also worth 50 marks. This section contains data-handling questions and a choice of one from two essay questions. The data-handling and practical skills questions are worth 25 marks. The essay is also worth 25 marks. It is recommended that you spend 30 minutes on the data-handling/practical skills questions, 15 minutes planning your essay and 30 minutes writing your essay.

Example of a Unit 7 question, with synoptic parts:
The cells that protect us from infection are the white blood cells. These cells have the ability to recognise the surface structure of every cell or biological molecule that exists in nature. Their ability to recognise non-self-molecules is due to the presence in embryos of stem cells, which give rise to the different kinds of white blood cell. The stem cells have several hundred genes in their DNA, coding for a variety of different receptor molecules that form part of the membrane of lymphocytes. These receptor molecules help the cells to recognise different biochemical groups.

When a stem cell divides, most of these genes are lost when the DNA is passed to each of the daughter lymphocytes. These losses are at random and each daughter lymphocyte is able to produce a different shape of receptor. Investigations into how these genes are inherited has forced a revolution in the way in which biologists think of DNA.

In embryonic life, all these millions of new lymphocytes randomly collide with the complementary molecules on cells of the developing embryo. As infection is very unlikely in the uterus, all the molecules encountered are self-molecules. The lymphocytes that react with the self-molecules usually die or are inactivated for life.

S (a) Describe how DNA is usually passed on to daughter cells during mitosis.
S (b) What is unusual about the way in which DNA is inherited during stem cell division, which has caused a revolution in the way biologists think of DNA?

Revision planning

Key words

A biological specification contains so many unfamiliar words it can appear to be a foreign language. It is important that you know the meaning of all of these words so that you know what is being asked in a question and can use the words correctly in your responses.

Below are some extracts from Module 7. The biological words that you need to know are in bold.

- Factors affecting **pathogenicity** of bacteria include:
  — features of the cell wall and capsule that affect attachment and entry to host cells
  — **exotoxins** and **endotoxins** produced by bacteria
  — **infectivity**
  — **invasiveness**

It is a good idea to go through the specification content listed in Content Guidance, underlining biological words and then writing a definition of each one. For example:
- **Exotoxin** — a toxin that is released by a living bacterium.
- **Endotoxin** — a toxin in the cell wall of a living bacterium.

This will give you the biology vocabulary that is essential both to understand and to answer questions.

Revision progress

You may find it useful to keep track of how your revision is going by drawing the table below, listing the topics in the first column.

Module topic	Revised (N/P/F)	Self-evaluation (1–5)
Bacteria	F	5
Culturing bacteria	F	4
Commercial biotechnology	F	3
Bacterial disease	P	2
Viral disease	N	
Protection against disease	N	

Complete column 2 to show how far you have got with your revision.
  N = not yet revised
  P = partly revised
  F = fully revised

Complete column 3 to show how confident you are with the topic.
  5 = I am confident I could answer any question on this topic
  1 = I found the practice questions very difficult

Update the table as your revision progresses.

Revising at home

- Revise regularly — do *not* leave revision until near the examination.
- Plan your revision carefully so that there is no last-minute rush.

- Revise in a quiet room — you cannot revise properly if distracted by the television or music.
- Revise in short stretches — work for half an hour, have a break for 10 minutes, then start again. You should be able to revise for about 2–3 hours in an evening.
- Revise actively — read a topic, then close your book and make a summary from memory. Then go back and see what you've missed.
- Do as many questions as possible from sample and past papers.

In the exam room

- Think before you write.
- Don't waste time copying out the question.
- Make a plan for longer answers.
- Think in paragraphs.
- Don't rush.
- Don't panic — if you can't do a question, go on to the next one.
- Check your spelling of words that are similar to others.

Content
Guidance

This section provides an overview of the key terms and concepts covered in **Module 7: Microbes and Disease**. The major facts that you need to learn are outlined and the principles you need to understand are explained. Some A2 questions will test recall while others will test understanding. For example, you could be given data about a particular antibiotic that you have never heard of and asked to explain how it has its effect.

The content of Module 7 falls into six main areas:

(1) Bacteria
The structure of bacteria, their nutrition and their reproduction.

(2) Culturing bacteria
Methods of growing bacteria, methods of monitoring their growth and the effects of external factors on their rate of growth.

(3) Commercial biotechnology
Methods of using microbes, and enzymes extracted from them, in industrial processes.

(4) Bacterial disease
Ways in which bacteria cause disease, with particular reference to food poisoning.

(5) Viral disease
The structure of viruses and the ways in which the influenza virus and HIV cause disease.

(6) Protection against disease
The body's natural defence mechanisms, vaccination and antibiotics.

Bacteria

Structure and function

Bacteria are prokaryotic cells, which means they do not have a distinct nucleus.

A generalised diagram of a bacterium is shown below.

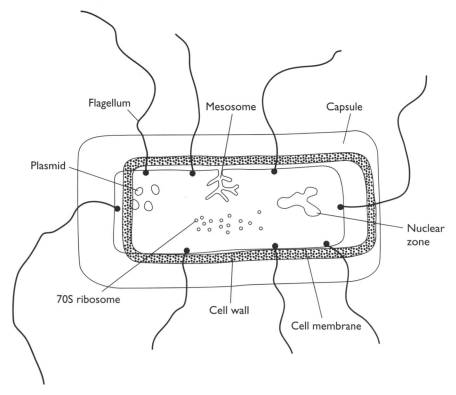

Cell wall — this is not made of cellulose, as plant cell walls are, but mainly of substances called peptidoglycans. The cell wall gives the bacterium its shape and prevents it bursting in hypotonic surroundings.

Cell membrane — a double phospholipid membrane with the same structure and functions as the cell membranes of higher organisms.

Nuclear zone — contains most of the nucleic acids. The nucleic acids contain most of the cell's genetic information. Bacterial cells have no nuclear membrane.

70S ribosomes — bacterial ribosomes are smaller than the 80S ribosomes of higher organisms. They have the same function, i.e. they are involved, along with RNA, in the translation phase of protein synthesis.

Mesosomes — infoldings of the cell membrane, which increase the surface area for enzyme activity. Mesosomes are the site of respiratory enzymes in all bacteria.

In those bacteria that can utilise light energy, the light-absorbing pigments occur on mesosomes. Bacteria do not have membrane-bound organelles, as higher organisms do.

Flagella — long, fine projections, capable of movement. Movement of the flagella brings about movement of the bacterium. Not all bacteria have flagella.

Plasmids — self-replicating, circular pieces of DNA found in most bacteria. They are not found in the nuclear region. Plasmids can be transferred between bacteria and so are important tools in genetic engineering.

Capsule — many types of bacteria have a slimy capsule outside the cell wall. This is usually made of polysaccharides. The capsule protects the bacterium both from attack by white blood cells and antibodies and from harmful substances in the environment.

> **Synoptic topic** Prokaryotic and eukaryotic cell structure

Nutrition

Most bacteria obtain energy in the same way as animal cells — by respiration. This involves the breakdown of organic compounds, such as sugars, to release energy. Most bacteria are aerobic. However, there are some anaerobic species that can survive in conditions where the oxygen concentration is low, for example waterlogged soils.

Some species of bacteria have pigments that trap light energy. They use this energy to drive the synthesis of carbohydrates and other organic compounds. In this respect, they are like green plants, although bacteria do not possess chloroplasts.

Some bacteria obtain energy by oxidising inorganic compounds. They use this energy to synthesise organic compounds. Nitrifying bacteria obtain energy either by oxidising ammonium ions to nitrite ions or by oxidising nitrite ions to nitrate ions.

Binary fission

Bacteria reproduce asexually by binary fission. This involves the semi-conservative replication of DNA, followed by infolding of the cell membrane to divide the cell contents into two. The daughter cells may then separate completely or they may remain attached to each other.

Binary fission is a rapid method of cell division. Bacteria undergo this form of division as long as external conditions are suitable.

> **Synoptic topic** Asexual reproduction and cloning

Culturing bacteria

Aseptic techniques

Conditions free of microorganisms are said to be **aseptic**. Aseptic techniques are used to prevent cultures becoming contaminated and to protect the health of personnel.

The procedure for transferring bacteria is as follows:
- Sterilise the inoculating loop in a Bunsen flame by heating it to red-heat.
- Flame the neck of the culture tube.
- Take a sample.
- Flame the neck of the culture tube again.
- Lift the Petri dish lid slightly to minimise contamination from the air and streak the sterile (autoclaved) agar plate with the sample.
- Sterilise the loop again.
- After the plate has been inoculated, it should be sealed.

In schools and colleges, cultures should be incubated at temperatures no higher than 25 °C. This slows the growth of most pathogenic bacteria, which have an optimum growth rate at 37 °C.

After they have been used, agar plates should be treated with disinfectants or autoclaved to destroy the bacteria. Autoclaving involves heating to a temperature of around 120 °C, using either pressure vessels or ovens.

Monitoring the growth of bacteria

A **total count** includes both living and dead bacterial cells; a **viable count** is live cells only. You should understand three methods of measuring the growth of bacteria in relation to total and viable counts:
- haemocytometry
- turbidimetry
- dilution plating

Haemocytometry

Haemocytometry involves counting bacteria under the microscope. A haemocytometer slide has squares ruled on it and there is a fixed depth between the slide and the coverslip.

The diagram overleaf shows bacteria on part of the central grid of a haemocytometer slide. You might be required to use the information to calculate the number of bacteria per cm^3.

First, calculate the volume under the coverslip.
- The large square has a side of 0.2 mm and a depth of 0.1 mm
- Its volume is $0.2 \times 0.2 \times 0.1 = 0.004 \, mm^3$

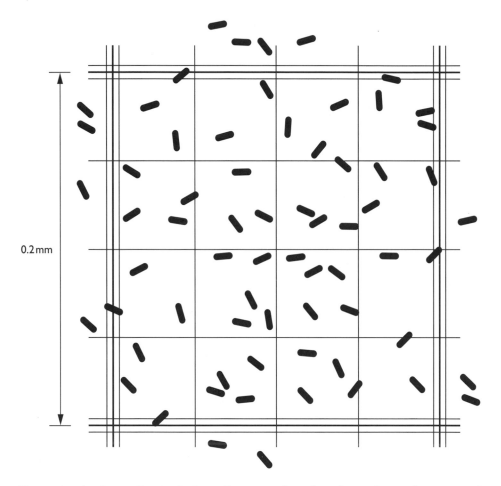

Use a standard counting technique. For example, where bacteria touch or cross the outside line, only include those on the north and east sides. Using this method, the total number of bacteria in the 0.2 mm square is 52.

Now calculate the number of bacteria.

- Number of bacteria per $mm^3 = \dfrac{52}{0.004} = 13\,000$
- Number of bacteria per $cm^3 = 13\,000 \times 10^3 = 13 \times 10^6 \ cm^{-3}$

This gives the **total cell count**. There is no method of knowing whether each bacterium is alive or dead.

Turbidimetry

Turbidimetry works on the principle that the more cells there are, the more turbid (cloudy) the broth culture is, i.e. the greater the percentage of light absorbed.

A colorimeter is used to measure either the percentage light transmitted or the amount of light absorbed in arbitrary optical density units.

A calibration curve is plotted using a direct count method, for example haemocytometry, on the same culture. This can be used to convert absorbance to numbers of microbes in future experiments on similar cultures. The diagram below shows a typical calibration graph. Turbidimetry gives a **total cell count**.

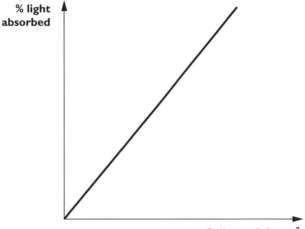

Dilution plating

Dilution plating involves first making serial dilutions, as shown in the diagram below.

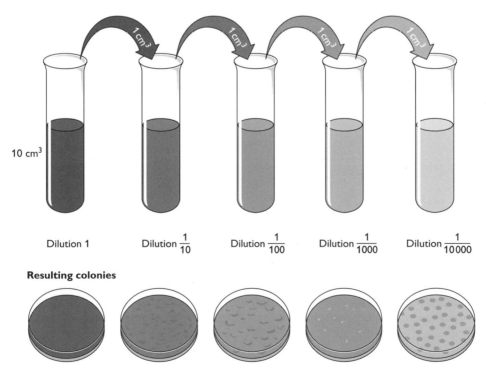

Using aseptic techniques:
- at each dilution, 1 cm^3 of solution is added to 9 cm^3 of sterile distilled water in a test tube, giving a ten-fold dilution factor
- a standard volume of each diluted sample is then used to inoculate an agar plate

Colonies are counted on plates where individual colonies can be distinguished. The number of bacteria is calculated from a plate with between 30 and 300 individual colonies. Each colony developed from a single microbe, so if the number of colonies is multiplied by the dilution factor, the number of bacteria in the original sample can be calculated.

This method gives a **viable cell count**, since only living bacteria divide to form colonies.

Total and viable counts

The diagram below shows what happens to the total and viable counts of bacteria, over time.

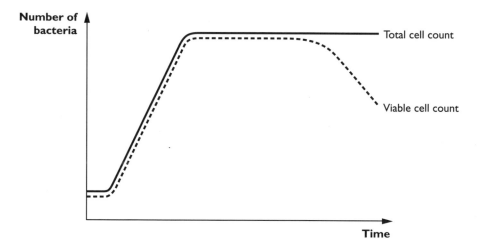

The reason for the fall in the viable count is usually environmental, for example lack of nutrient, lack of oxygen, or the poisonous effect of a bacterial waste product.

Population growth pattern

Typical growth curve

The graph below shows a typical growth curve for a bacterial culture.

A–B is the **lag** phase. There is little cell division because it takes time for the bacteria to synthesise ribosomes and produce enzymes that are capable of breaking down the new substrate.

B–C is the **exponential** phase. The rate of cell division is at a maximum because there are no limiting factors.

C–D is the **stationary** phase. Bacteria are being produced and dying at the same rate, as some factor(s) becomes limiting.

D–E is the **death** phase. More bacteria are dying than are being produced owing to a critical limiting factor, for example lack of a nutrient.

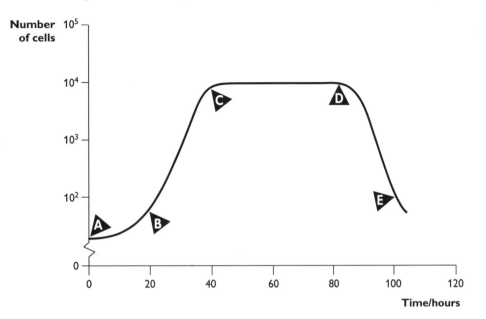

Effects of external factors on growth

Temperature

The graph below shows the effect of temperature on the growth of bacteria.

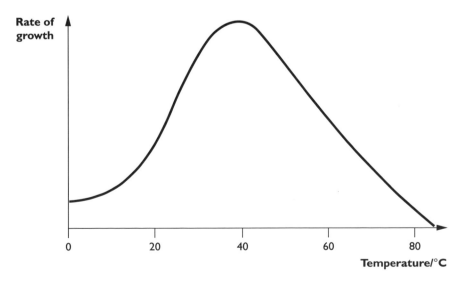

The shape of the graph is roughly the same for all bacteria, but the optimum temperature depends on the bacterial species and covers a wide range.

Generally, an increase in temperature increases bacterial growth rate because the rate of metabolism is increased. However, high temperatures denature the tertiary structure of proteins, reducing bacterial activity.

Some bacteria have proteins that are resistant to high temperatures, for example those found in hot springs. Do not assume that all living organisms work best at human body temperature.

pH
Most bacteria grow best at pH 6.5. Extremes of pH denature the tertiary structure of proteins and therefore slow the rate of growth.

Nutrient availability
Microbes need:

- a carbon source, for example carbohydrate, for energy
- a nitrogen source, for example ammonium or nitrite ions (only a few can use gaseous nitrogen)
- raw material for synthetic reactions

Many microbes need organic nitrogen, for example amino acids, and some require particular vitamins (e.g. vitamin B_1) and/or minerals (e.g. sodium).

Therefore, lack of a nutrient often limits growth rate.

Oxygen availability
Most microbes require oxygen for aerobic respiration to produce the ATP needed to drive the synthetic reactions that produce materials for growth. Some gut bacteria, for example, need only 5–10% oxygen for growth. Most microbes use anaerobic respiration if oxygen supplies are insufficient for oxygen needs.

Synoptic topics Tertiary structure of proteins, respiration

Bioassay

Bioassay means using living organisms to measure something. For example, bacterial lawns can be used to determine the effectiveness of antibiotics and disinfectants. Using aseptic techniques, the nutrient agar in a Petri dish is flooded with a suspension of bacteria. The disinfectant or antibiotic is usually applied by adding a standard-sized piece of sterile filter paper soaked in the appropriate solution. Antibiotic discs are also available commercially. The antibiotic or disinfectant inhibits the growth of the bacteria because it diffuses into the agar.

A plate testing four different antibiotics or disinfectants is shown in the diagram below. The clear zone around each of the pieces of paper, A to D, indicates where bacterial growth is inhibited. The larger the clear area, the more effective is the antibiotic or disinfectant. In this case, C is the most effective and D the least effective.

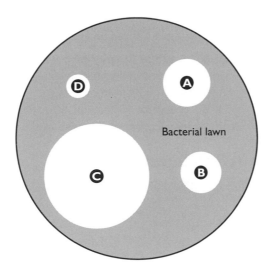

The higher the concentration of antibiotic, the greater the concentration gradient and the faster is the diffusion rate, resulting in a wider inhibition zone.

Commercial biotechnology

Screening procedures

Microbes are useful in industry because they:

- have simple nutrient requirements
- have fast growth rates
- can be genetically manipulated to produce valuable products
- can be grown on cheap or waste feedstocks
- generally do not produce pollutants (toxic by-products)

Wild microorganisms are screened to find strains that satisfy the above criteria. The diagram below shows how fungi may be screened for antibiotic production.

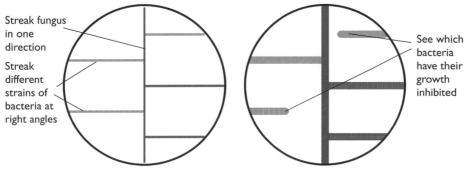

Incubate for 3–7 days at 25 °C

Fungi that show significant inhibition of several types of bacteria might be further investigated to see if they satisfy the other criteria listed above.

In a similar way, bacteria can be screened for protease production. Agar plates containing the protein casein, which makes the agar cloudy, are used. The plate is inoculated with different bacteria. If bacteria produce protease, the casein will be hydrolysed, producing a clear area. The greater the clear area that develops around a bacterial colony, the greater is the production of protease by the bacteria.

Continuous and batch cultures

Microorganisms can be grown in either **batch culture** or **continuous culture**.

In batch culture:
- the substrate is added at the start
- the products are harvested at the end
- the cells are in the exponential growth phase for a limited period
- the amount of product is limited by the initial amount of substrate

The procedure is therefore less productive than continuous culture, but it is easier to control factors and contamination is less likely.

In continuous culture:
- fresh substrate is added continuously
- the product is harvested continuously
- the cells are maintained in the exponential growth phase
- the amount of product is virtually unlimited

The process is therefore more productive than batch culture, but it is difficult to control factors and contamination is more likely.

Useful products from microorganisms

Penicillin
Penicillin is produced industrially using a high-yielding strain of the mould *Penicillium chrysogenum*.

Fermentation
The mould is grown in a fermenter. A simplified diagram of a fermenter is shown below.

- Air is needed to provide oxygen for aerobic respiration.
- The water jacket is needed to maintain constant temperature. Heat is needed initially; heat produced by respiration of the mould is removed at later stages.
- The stirrer distributes heat and ensures even aeration — this is particularly important as the cell mass increases and the medium becomes thicker.
- Aseptic conditions must be maintained to prevent the growth of unwanted microbes.

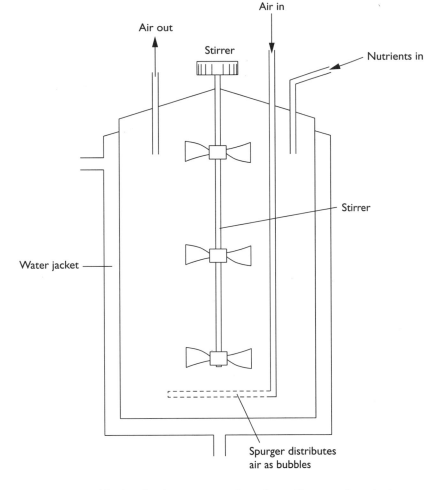

The process is started by incubating a suspension of mould spores in a starter medium. This starter medium is then placed in the fermenter along with nutrients. The main nutrient provided for the mould is a by-product of starch manufacture called corn steep liquor. Additional nutrients are a carbon source (e.g. lactose) and an organic nitrogen source (e.g. yeast extract).

The culture is maintained at 24 °C and slightly alkaline pH for a week. Penicillin production does not begin until about 40 hours, when the exponential growth phase is completed.

Downstream processing

Since penicillin is taken as a drug by humans, it must be highly purified. The purification is known as **downstream processing**. The major stages are outlined below:

- **Filtration** — a rotating drum separates mould mycelium from the filtrate containing penicillin.

- **Solvent extraction** — butylacetate is used as a solvent. Using a membrane in conjunction with countercurrent flow increases the rate of extraction.
- **Crystallisation** — adding potassium salts produces a potassium salt of penicillin, which is insoluble in butylacetate and therefore precipitates.
- **Filter, wash, dry** — the crystals are filtered off, then washed and dried. The product is almost 100% pure.

Isolated enzymes

Microorganisms have been used to create useful products throughout recorded history; the large-scale use of purified microbial enzymes is relatively recent.

Enzymes are preferred to whole microorganisms for two main reasons:
- The concentration of the enzyme is higher, leading to a faster reaction rate.
- The product is purer — only one reaction takes place because there is only one enzyme. Whole microorganisms contain many enzymes, giving rise to many end products. This necessitates costly downstream processing.

Immobilised enzymes

Enzymes are expensive to produce. A process is therefore more cost-effective if the enzyme can be used repeatedly. One method of doing this is to immobilise the enzyme. If an enzyme is immobilised, it can be used in continuous rather than batch processes.

Methods of immobilising enzymes
Adsorption to a matrix
This is fairly easy to do and can achieve loadings of up to 1 g enzyme per 1 g of matrix. Adsorbents commonly used include porous carbon, clays, metal oxides and resins. The links between the matrix and the enzyme are quite weak, so care must be taken not to wash off the enzyme.

Bonding the enzyme with a cross-linking agent
Strong covalent links are produced between the enzyme and its support by using another chemical to cross-link the enzyme to the support. Such molecules include amino acids and glutaraldehyde. The advantage of this method is that the enzyme is held more strongly than by adsorption, but the loading that can be achieved is much lower.

Entrapment
Enzymes can be trapped in the pores of gels or fibres. The most common method of entrapment is in sodium alginate beads. The enzyme is mixed with sodium alginate and syringed dropwise into calcium chloride solution. The calcium ions cross-link the alginate, trapping the enzymes inside insoluble calcium alginate beads. This method does not damage enzymes.

 **Synoptic topic** Enzyme action

Bacterial disease

Pathogenicity

Pathogenicity is the ability of bacteria to produce disease. Factors influencing pathogenicity are outlined below.

Attachment methods

Some bacteria have projections called **pili**. These attach to receptors such as mannose receptors on the outside of host cells. Some of the bacteria that cause genitourinary tract infections, for example gonorrhoea, have these structures.

Some bacteria have a capsule that contains a sticky polysaccharide. This helps the bacterium to attach to a host cell. Some of the staphylococci that cause skin infections attach themselves in this way.

Toxins

Many symptoms of disease are caused by **toxins**, which are chemicals produced by bacteria.

Exotoxins are released by living bacteria as they grow. An example is coagulase, which is produced by staphylococci and causes abscesses. Cholera toxin increases water and ion loss from host cells, resulting in diarrhoea.

Endotoxins are found in the cell walls of Gram-negative bacteria. They are released when the cells die and the wall disintegrates. The release of endotoxins usually produces fever in the host.

Infectivity

Infectivity is the number of bacteria needed to produce the disease. Ten million bacteria need to be taken in with food to produce *Salmonella* food poisoning, but only a few typhoid bacteria are needed to produce typhoid.

Invasiveness

Invasiveness is the ability of bacteria to spread within the body. It is often determined by bacterial enzymes, which break down tissues, allowing the bacteria wider access. Some of these enzymes, fibrinolysins, break down blood clots and are distributed throughout the body by the blood system.

Transmission

Food-borne infection

Salmonella food poisoning is caused by many species of *Salmonella* but the most common is *Salmonella enteritidis*. These bacteria are rod-shaped and have long flagella which enable them to move.

The bacteria are found in the gut of most farm animals. Meat may become infected with the bacteria when the animal is slaughtered. However, if the meat is refrigerated immediately after slaughter there is little bacterial growth. Bacteria are passed onto the skin of people who handle the meat and may then be transferred to other food. If this food is not kept refrigerated, the bacteria will grow and divide to produce enough bacteria to cause an infection in anyone who eats the food.

Some people are carriers of *Salmonella* — they excrete the bacteria in their faeces but show no symptoms of the disease. If these people do not wash their hands after defaecating, they may pass the bacteria onto food and thence to other people.

The symptoms of *Salmonella* food poisoning are abdominal pains, slight fever, sickness and diarrhoea. Diarrhoea is treated by rehydrating the patient. This involves drinking a solution of ions in water, to replace the water and ions lost by the body.

Control measures for *Salmonella* food poisoning are:
- improving hygiene methods in food handlers, for example through hand washing and the use of disposable plastic gloves when handling meat
- keeping raw meat and fresh meat separated
- thorough defrosting of meat, particularly chicken, before cooking
- thorough cooking of meat
- if meat is reheated, then it must be heated to an internal temperature of at least 60 °C

Water-borne infection

Most cases of water-borne diarrhoeal infection are caused by *Escherichia coli*. Everyone has this bacterium in his or her large intestine and most strains are harmless. Some strains, however, have a similar effect to *Salmonella* — they cause the cells lining the intestine to lose ions and water.

This form of diarrhoea is contracted by drinking water contaminated with faeces. It can be avoided by drinking only water that has been chlorinated to kill the bacteria or by drinking bottled water from springs that are not contaminated by faeces.

On a large scale, proper disposal of faeces and the prevention of contamination of water are key control measures. Examples include covering reservoirs and preventing animal access to catchment areas.

Viral disease

Characteristics of viruses

The structure of the human immunodeficiency virus (HIV) is illustrated below. All viruses possess nucleic acid and a protein coat called a **capsid**, which protects the nucleic acid. HIV has an additional inner capsid. It also has an outer phospholipid coat with glycoprotein pegs. These pegs help the virus to attach to the membrane of a host cell.

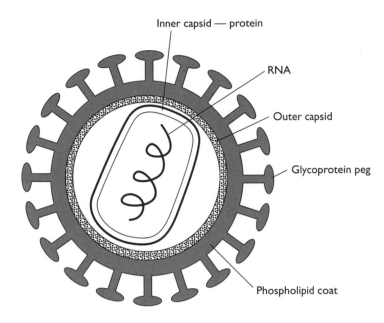

The influenza virus is similar to HIV. However, it does not have an inner capsid and its glycoprotein pegs do not have knobs on the end.

Transmission

Influenza

Influenza is caused by an air-borne virus. Infected people breathe out the virus, which is then inhaled by other people. The virus enters the cells lining the respiratory system and reproduces inside the cells. The cells then burst, releasing the new virus particles. The incubation period is about 3 days. Bursting of the cells releases toxins that produce the symptoms — fever, headache, tiredness and body aches. Secondary infection of the damaged area by bacteria may cause additional symptoms. The infection can last 1–2 weeks. There is no cure for influenza; the treatment is to keep warm, rest and drink plenty of fluids.

HIV

HIV is a virus that enters T-lymphocyte cells in the blood and reproduces.

The most common methods of infection are unprotected sexual activity and the sharing of infected needles. The semen of an infected man and the vaginal secretions of an infected woman contain infected T-lymphocytes. These enter the blood through small lesions produced during the sex act. Hypodermic needles used by people infected with HIV will transmit infected T-lymphocytes to another person if the needle is not first sterilised. Some people have been infected with HIV through blood transfused from an infected person.

People infected with HIV produce antibodies to combat the spread of the disease. When these antibodies can be detected, the person is said to be HIV-positive. This is not the same as having AIDS (acquired immune deficiency syndrome), but the majority of HIV-positive people go on to develop AIDS. Drugs are now available to delay the onset of AIDS.

Replication

Both the influenza virus and HIV reproduce inside the host cells, but they use different methods of producing new nucleic acids. The influenza virus replicates its RNA directly in the host cell nucleus. The RNA code for HIV is transcribed to viral DNA, using the enzyme reverse transcriptase. This DNA then enters the nucleus where it is transcribed into virus RNA. Both cells use host cell translation to produce capsid proteins and glycoproteins.

Similarities and differences between the influenza virus and HIV replication are shown in the following flow charts.

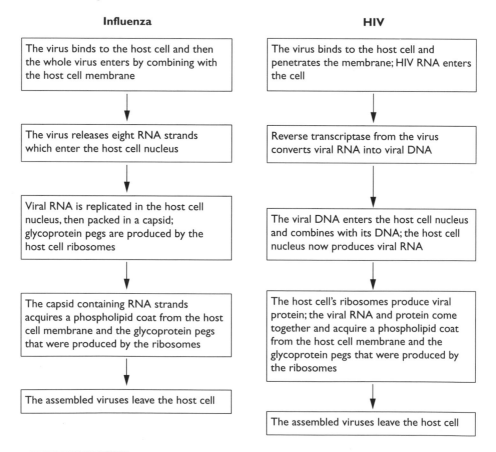

Influenza

The virus binds to the host cell and then the whole virus enters by combining with the host cell membrane

↓

The virus releases eight RNA strands which enter the host cell nucleus

↓

Viral RNA is replicated in the host cell nucleus, then packed in a capsid; glycoprotein pegs are produced by the host cell ribosomes

↓

The capsid containing RNA strands acquires a phospholipid coat from the host cell membrane and the glycoprotein pegs that were produced by the ribosomes

↓

The assembled viruses leave the host cell

HIV

The virus binds to the host cell and penetrates the membrane; HIV RNA enters the cell

↓

Reverse transcriptase from the virus converts viral RNA into viral DNA

↓

The viral DNA enters the host cell nucleus and combines with its DNA; the host cell nucleus now produces viral RNA

↓

The host cell's ribosomes produce viral protein; the viral RNA and protein come together and acquire a phospholipid coat from the host cell membrane and the glycoprotein pegs that were produced by the ribosomes

↓

The assembled viruses leave the host cell

Synoptic topics DNA, RNA, translation, transcription

How viruses cause disease

Viruses reproduce inside host cells. Every infected host cell dies as the new viruses are released. Usually, toxins produced by the host cell are released at the same time. It is these toxins that cause disease symptoms such as fevers, headaches, aches and pains.

How HIV causes AIDS

HIV infects T-lymphocytes, which are an important part of the body's immune system. Eventually, the T-lymphocytes release HIV into the blood. These viruses infect large numbers of T-lymphocytes, which in turn release large numbers of HIV. Thus, large numbers of T-lymphocytes are destroyed and the body loses part of its immune system. The body now becomes more susceptible to other diseases. Most AIDS patients eventually die from infections such as pneumonia, against which they have no defence.

Treatment and prevention of viral infections

Viral infections are difficult to treat because the virus exists inside host cells and cannot be reached by any drugs that are administered. Killing a virus inside a cell inevitably means killing the cell as well.

Most drugs that are used against bacteria work by affecting the cell wall, the cell membrane or the cell metabolism. Viruses have no cell wall, no cell membrane and no intrinsic metabolism, so anti-bacterial drugs are ineffective against them.

HIV and the influenza virus both have a high mutation rate with respect to the number and type of glycoproteins in their coats. Therefore, vaccination against this year's version of the influenza virus may not be effective against next year's strain, because the body's defence cells may not recognise the new version of the virus. There is no HIV vaccine.

You are expected to be able to suggest strategies for reducing the incidence of influenza and preventing the spread of HIV. For influenza, these include annual vaccination of people at risk and avoiding places with poor ventilation. For HIV, the major preventatives are campaigns promoting protected sex, and provision of clean needles for addicts.

Protection against disease

Natural defence mechanisms

The first line of defence for the body is to prevent microorganisms gaining access to its living cells. Ways of doing this are outlined below.

Skin has an outermost layer of dead cells. These cells are hardened by a substance called **keratin**, which makes it difficult for microorganisms to penetrate. Glands in the skin secrete fatty acids and lactic acid, which inhibit the growth of micro-organisms.

Tears contain an enzyme called **lysozyme**, which kills microorganisms by breaking down their cell walls.

Mucus is secreted by the cells lining the respiratory tract. It is also present in saliva and tears. Mucus contains a protein called **IgA**. This protein acts as an antibody to many species of bacteria. Mucus is sticky and traps microorganisms in the air we breathe in. The mucus is then moved to the throat by ciliated cells and subsequently swallowed. In the stomach, the microorganisms are attacked by acid and enzymes.

Saliva contains the IgA antibody which kills some species of microorganism.

Cilia are tiny hair-like projections on the surface of epithelial cells in some parts of the body. In the respiratory tract, they move mucus to the throat. They do not themselves trap bacteria.

Phagocytosis

The types of white blood cell produced by the body are illustrated below. All are concerned with defence, but they function in different ways.

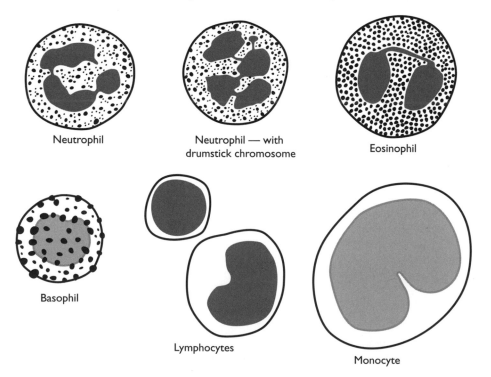

Neutrophil

Neutrophil — with drumstick chromosome

Eosinophil

Basophil

Lymphocytes

Monocyte

Neutrophils are the most common type of white blood cell. They are attracted to the site of an infection by chemicals released by the damaged cells. They have receptors in their outer membranes that bind with proteins or carbohydrates in the cell wall of the microorganism. This stimulates the neutrophil to engulf the microorganism by enclosing it in a vacuole. Enzymes packaged by the Golgi body are then secreted into the vacuole and the microorganism is digested.

Some **monocytes** develop into cells called **macrophages**. These leave the blood to become lodged in organs such as the liver, lungs, gut and spleen. They engulf and digest microorganisms in the same way as neutrophils.

The immune response

The body recognises foreign cells or particles by their antigens. Most antigens are proteins, polysaccharides or glycoproteins. Antigens are found:

- on the cell surface of a microorganism
- on the surface of a virus
- on the cell surface of a tissue or organ transplant
- as toxins produced by microorganisms

These antigens are recognised by receptors in the cell membranes of several types of blood cell.

Cell-mediated immunity

There are two main types of lymphocyte: T-lymphocytes and B-lymphocytes. T-lymphocytes attack microorganisms directly. The sequence of events is shown in the following flow chart.

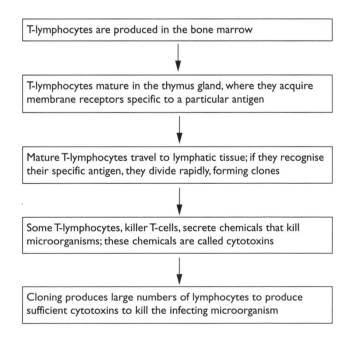

T-lymphocytes are produced in the bone marrow

↓

T-lymphocytes mature in the thymus gland, where they acquire membrane receptors specific to a particular antigen

↓

Mature T-lymphocytes travel to lymphatic tissue; if they recognise their specific antigen, they divide rapidly, forming clones

↓

Some T-lymphocytes, killer T-cells, secrete chemicals that kill microorganisms; these chemicals are called cytotoxins

↓

Cloning produces large numbers of lymphocytes to produce sufficient cytotoxins to kill the infecting microorganism

Antibody-mediated immunity

B-lymphocytes protect the body from microorganisms by producing antibodies. The sequence of events is illustrated in the following flow chart.

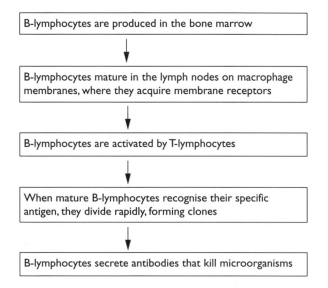

B-lymphocytes are produced in the bone marrow

↓

B-lymphocytes mature in the lymph nodes on macrophage membranes, where they acquire membrane receptors

↓

B-lymphocytes are activated by T-lymphocytes

↓

When mature B-lymphocytes recognise their specific antigen, they divide rapidly, forming clones

↓

B-lymphocytes secrete antibodies that kill microorganisms

Antibodies

The structure of an antibody is shown below.

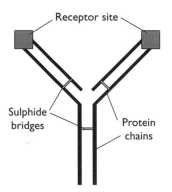

Receptor site

Sulphide bridges

Protein chains

Every antibody has the same basic Y shape, made from protein molecules held together by sulphide bridges. However, the receptor site of each antibody is unique and specific to one type of antigen.

The antibody may form a complex with its specific antigen on the surface of a micro-organism. What happens next depends on the type of antibody.

- Some antibodies cause microorganisms to stick together. This process is called **agglutination**. Macrophages quickly detect the agglutinated microorganisms and engulf them.

- Some antibodies stimulate phagocytes to engulf microorganisms.
- Some antibodies cause the toxins produced by microorganisms to precipitate out, thereby becoming harmless.
- Some antibodies prevent microorganisms attaching to cell membranes.

Synoptic topic Protein structure

Immunological memory

Both B-lymphocytes and T-lymphocytes may form **memory cells**. Memory T-lymphocytes remain in the lymph nodes. If microorganisms with their specific type of antigen enter the body, the memory T-cells divide rapidly to form clones that produce cytotoxins to kill the invader.

Memory B-lymphocytes remain in the lymph nodes for many years. If they detect a microorganism with the specific antigen, they clone rapidly, producing large numbers of B-cells, all of which quickly secrete antibodies against the microorganism.

The result of this is that a second exposure to the antigen brings a much bigger response in terms of antibody production.

The initial production of antibodies is called the **primary response**. The second, larger response is called the **secondary response**. These responses are important in vaccination procedures. They are shown on the graphs below.

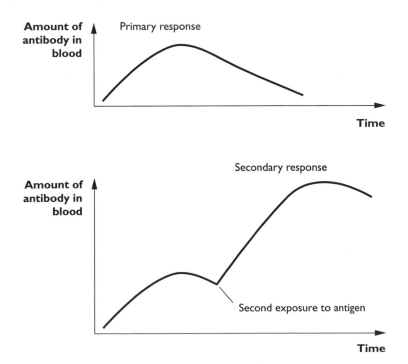

Vaccination

Immunisation provokes an immune response by introducing a vaccine, so that the person will produce memory B-cells and memory T-cells against the microorganism. If the person comes in contact with the microorganism, the immune response will be rapid and the person will be unlikely to develop the disease.

There are different types of vaccine, all of which provoke the immune response.

Dead, virulent microorganisms — the whooping cough vaccine consists of dead microorganisms. However, the antigens in the cell walls of the microorganisms still stimulate activation of B-cells and T-cells.

Live, weakened strains of microorganisms — a weakened form of rubella has been produced by selective breeding over many generations. It produces the same immune response as the virulent virus, but does not produce severe disease symptoms.

Modified version of a toxin — the severe symptoms of diphtheria are caused by a toxin released by the bacteria. A modified version of this toxin has been produced, which although it produces symptoms, stimulates the production of antibodies that precipitate the toxin.

Isolated antigens — the influenza vaccine is produced by extracting antigens from the virus. These provoke the immune response without introducing the virus, which would multiply in the body.

Genetically engineered antigens — the hepatitis B vaccine contains only genetically engineered antigens.

Most vaccines are administered by injection, since they would be digested if taken orally. A few, however, can be taken orally (e.g. polio).

Passive immunity

If a person has been exposed to a dangerous infection to which they are not immune, immediate protection can be given by injecting antibodies against the microorganism. These antibodies are produced by giving a vaccine to animals, then separating the antibodies they have produced from their blood. This method gives only temporary protection, since the antibodies do not provoke an immune response (only antigens do that). The body will soon destroy the antibodies, so the person will no longer be protected.

Babies receive passive immunity if their mothers breast-feed them in the days immediately after birth. During this period, the breasts produce a liquid called colostrum, which contains antibodies effective against many different diseases. The antibodies do not provoke an immune response, so this passive immunity lasts only for a few months.

Antibiotics

An antibiotic is a substance produced by a microorganism that inhibits the growth of other microorganisms. Many antibiotics are produced on a large scale in fermenters (see page 22).

Antibiotics work in several different ways. These include:
- preventing cell wall synthesis — penicillin inhibits enzymes that build up cross-linkages between the molecules that make up the bacterial cell wall
- disrupting cell membranes — polymyxin B binds to phospholipids in the cell membrane of the bacterium and interferes with its function as a selective barrier
- affecting nucleic acid synthesis — rifampin interferes with RNA synthesis in bacteria by binding to a subunit on the enzyme responsible for replication of RNA
- affecting protein synthesis — clindamycin inhibits protein synthesis in bacteria

Antibiotics that are effective against a wide range of microorganisms are called broad-spectrum antibiotics. Those that are effective against only a few species of microorganisms are known as narrow-spectrum antibiotics. The effectiveness of antibiotics against different species of microorganism can be assayed by the method described on page 20.

Synoptic topics Cell structure, protein synthesis, nucleic acids

Antibiotic resistance

Some species of bacteria are resistant to certain antibiotics. Resistance mechanisms include:
- secreting enzymes to break down the antibiotic
- development of a capsule resistant to antibiotics
- decreasing the permeability of the cell membrane to antibiotics

The resistance may have arisen via mutation. For example, some strains of bacteria can secrete the enzyme penicillinase, which breaks down penicillin. Using penicillin will kill all the bacteria that do not secrete penicillinase. Soon, only resistant bacteria remain. The gene for penicillinase production is located on a plasmid in the resistant strain. Bacteria have a form of reproduction in which they pair and exchange plasmids. In this way the penicillinase gene can be transferred to non-resistant strains.

The appearance of resistant strains has intensified research to find new types of antibiotic to which they are not resistant. It has also led to calls for antibiotics to be prescribed only when essential and to the banning of their use in animal feeds.

Synoptic topics Mutation, natural selection

Questions
&
Answers

In this section of the guide there are 10 questions based on the topic areas outlined in the Content Guidance section. The section is structured as follows:

- sample questions in the style of the module
- example candidate responses mostly at the C/D boundary, though sometimes as low as grade E (Candidate A) — these answers demonstrate some strengths but many weaknesses, with potential for improvement
- example candidate responses at the A/B boundary (Candidate B) — these answers demonstrate thorough knowledge, a good understanding and an ability to deal with the data that are presented in the questions. There is, however, still some room for improvement

Some parts of the questions simply ask you to recall basic facts. Other parts contain material with which you are unfamiliar. Before answering these, ask yourself 'Which biological principle is this addressing?' Write down the principle (in rough) and then work out how the principle applies to the data. In calculations, always show your working, and when reading graphs, always draw lines between the plot in question and the axes.

Questions preceded by the icon **S** are synoptic — you will need knowledge and understanding of principles from other modules to answer them.

Examiner's comments

All candidate responses are followed by examiner's comments. These are preceded by the icon **e** and indicate where credit is due. In the weaker answers, they also point out areas for improvement, specific problems and common errors such as lack of clarity, weak or non-existent development, irrelevance, misinterpretation of the question and mistaken meanings of words.

Question 1

Bacteria

The diagram below shows a bacterium.

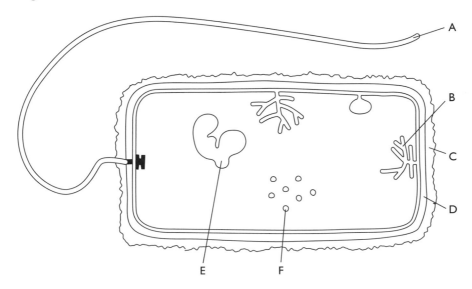

(a) Name the parts labelled A to F.   (6 marks)
(b) (i) Describe the function of part A.   (1 mark)
    (ii) Describe the function of part B.   (1 mark)
(c) Describe differences between the ways in which genetic information is stored in
    bacterial cells and in human body cells.   (3 marks)

Total: 11 marks

■ ■ ■

Answer to question 1: candidate A

(a) A — cilium; B — mesosome; C — capsid; D — cell wall; E — plasmid; F — ribosome

> ℯ B, D and F are correct, for 3 marks. The candidate has confused cilium with
> **flagellum** for A; capsid with **capsule** for C; and plasmid with **chromosome** (nuclear
> zone) for E.

(b) (i) It helps the bacterium to swim.

> ℯ This receives the mark, but it would be better to refer to movement rather than
> swimming.

(ii) It increases the surface area for diffusion of oxygen.

> ℯ This scores nothing. The candidate has confused the diffusion of oxygen in gaseous
> exchange with the chemical reactions of **respiration**.

(c) The bacterium stores its genetic material in its chromosome and in its plasmid, whereas the human cell just stores it in chromosomes.

 This receives just 1 mark, for mentioning that bacteria have plasmids whereas human cells do not.

■ ■ ■

Answer to question 1: candidate B

(a) A — flagellum; B — mesosome; C — capsule; D — cell wall; E — nucleic acids; F — plasmid

 This receives 5 marks out of 6. For F, the candidate has confused plasmids with **ribosomes**.

(b) (i) Locomotion

 Correct, for 1 mark.

(ii) It provides a large surface area.

 This answer is incomplete and scores nothing. The mark would have been obtained if the candidate had added '**for attachment of respiratory enzymes**'.

(c) The genetic information is stored on several chromosomes in the nucleus of a human cell. The bacterial cell has no nucleus. It has only one, long chromosome. In addition, some genetic information is stored in its plasmids.

 This is a good answer, for full marks.

Culturing bacteria (I)

A bacterium was grown in a liquid culture medium. Every hour, a 1 cm^3 sample was taken and diluted 100 times. One drop of the diluted sample was placed on a haemocytometer slide. The number of bacteria in several large squares was counted and the mean number in each 0.004 mm^3 was then calculated. The results are shown on the graph.

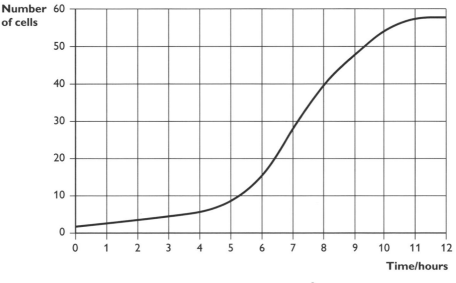

(a) Use the graph to calculate the number of bacteria in 1 cm^3 of the culture after 7 hours. (2 marks)

(b) Explain the shape of the graph:
  (i) between 0 and 4 hours
  (ii) between 6 and 9 hours
  (iii) between 11 and 12 hours (6 marks)

(c) Describe how you would find the number of viable cells in the 12-hour culture. (3 marks)

Total: 11 marks

■ ■ ■

Answer to question 2: candidate A

(a) 2800

> 🅔 This scores nothing. The candidate has simply multiplied by the dilution factor, ignoring the volume of the haemocytometer count.

(b) (i) This is the lag phase. The bacteria are not dividing very rapidly.

> 🅔 This receives 1 mark only, because there is no *reason* given for the slow cell division.

(ii) This is the log phase. The bacteria are dividing rapidly.

ℓ This receives 1 mark only, because there is no *reason* given for the rapid cell division.

(iii) This is the stationary phase. The bacteria have stopped dividing.

ℓ This scores nothing. It is a common error to state that division has stopped in this phase, rather than that cells are dividing at the same rate as they are dying.

(c) I would pipette $1\,cm^3$ of the sample onto an agar plate. After incubating the plate, I would count the number of colonies, then multiply to get the answer.

ℓ This receives 2 marks for taking a standard sample and for counting colonies after incubation. The final mark would have been gained for taking a standard sample of the diluted culture.

■ ■ ■

Answer to question 2: candidate B

(a) $28 \times \dfrac{1}{0.004} = 7000$

ℓ This receives 1 mark. The candidate has calculated the correct number for $1\,mm^3$ of the diluted sample, but has not multiplied by the dilution factor. The correct answer is 700 000.

(b) (i) The bacteria are not dividing very rapidly. This may be due to the time taken for the bacteria to produce enzymes to use the nutrients.

ℓ This is an appropriate answer, for full marks.

(ii) The bacteria are dividing most rapidly. This is because there are no factors limiting their growth.

ℓ This is a good answer, for full marks.

(iii) This is the stationary phase. There is now a limiting factor.

ℓ This receives 1 mark. The reason is correct, but there is no reference to the **rates of cell division and cell death being equal.**

(c) Transfer $1\,cm^3$ of the diluted sample onto an agar plate. Incubate the plate at $25\,°C$ for 24 hours. Count the number of colonies, then multiply by the dilution factor.

ℓ This is correct, for full marks.

Culturing bacteria (II)

(a) Describe the aseptic techniques you would use when transferring bacteria from a stock culture tube to an agar plate. Give a reason for each technique you describe. (8 marks)

(b) An investigation was carried out into the effectiveness of four different anti-bacterial spray solutions used to clean surfaces in a kitchen. An identical paper disc was soaked in each spray solution and placed on a lawn of *Salmonella* in a Petri dish. The diagram below shows the appearance of the Petri dish after incubation.

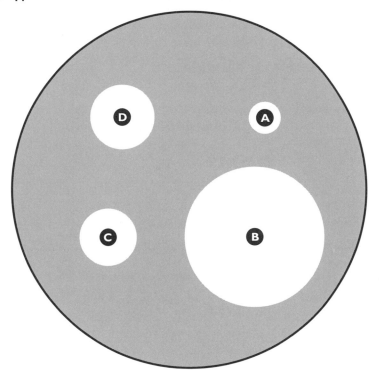

(i) Explain the results of the investigation. (3 marks)

(ii) Suggest a control for the investigation. Explain the reasons for your choice. (2 marks)

Total: 13 marks

■ ■ ■

Answer to question 3: candidate A

(a) First, I would sterilise an inoculating loop by flaming. This kills the bacteria on it. Then I would dip the loop into the culture to get some bacteria onto it. Then I would lift the lid of the Petri dish and gently rub the inoculating loop onto the agar to transfer the bacteria. I would then seal the dish.

e This receives 4 marks. There is no reference to **flaming the neck of the culture tube**, and the reasons for some of the steps are omitted.

(b) (i) B was the most effective spray because more bacteria were killed.

e This receives 1 mark. There is no reference to the **clear zones** or to **different zone widths**.

(ii) Use an identical, sterile piece of paper with no spray solution.

e This is a reasonable suggestion, gaining 1 mark since no spray was used, but the paper should have been wet rather than dry.

■ ■ ■

Answer to question 3: candidate B

(a) An inoculating loop is flamed, then allowed to cool. The neck of the culture tube is then flamed. This means that air moves out of the tube when the stopper is removed. The inoculating loop is used to transfer bacteria from the tube to the agar. When doing this the lid of the Petri dish is only lifted a little. The loop is re-flamed and the dish is then sealed.

e This receives 7 marks. The only omission is the reason for only lifting the lid of the dish a little.

(b) (i) The clear zone around each disc indicates where bacteria have been killed by the spray solution. Disc B has the widest clear zone, so B is the most effective spray.

e This is a good answer, for full marks.

(ii) Use paper dipped in sterile water.

e This is a reasonable suggestion for 1 mark, but to gain full marks the candidate should have explained why sterile water should be used (it does not contain microorganisms).

Question Q4

Commercial biotechnology (I)

(a) Explain why penicillin is made using a batch process rather than a continuous process. (2 marks)

(b) Describe the downstream processing of penicillin. (5 marks)

(c) The graph below shows some changes that take place during production of an antibiotic.

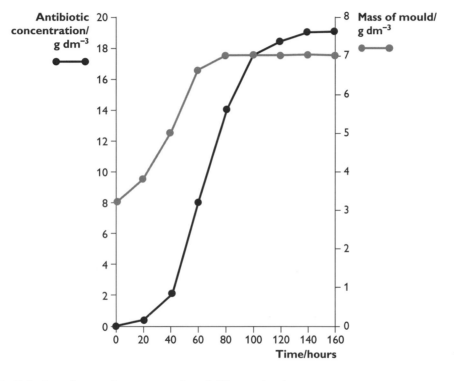

(i) Calculate the maximum rate of penicillin production. (3 marks)

(ii) Explain why the mass of the mould remains constant after 80 hours. (2 marks)

Total: 12 marks

Answer to question 4: candidate A

(a) This is because the fungus needs a long time to produce the penicillin.

> *e* This receives 1 mark for the idea of the length of time needed to produce penicillin, but there is no reason given for the use of batch rather than continuous culture.

(b) The fungus is filtered off. The penicillin is then precipitated. It is then dried.

> *e* This is a good answer, for 3 marks. All that is missing is *detail* of precipitation and **filtration after precipitation**.

(c) (i) $19 \, \mathrm{g \, dm^{-3}}$

e This scores no marks. The candidate has assumed the units on the vertical axis refer to a rate.

(ii) It has reached the stationary phase.

e This scores no marks. There is no reference to **growth** or to **nutrient depletion**.

■ ■ ■

Answer to question 4: candidate B

(a) This is because the fungus does not produce penicillin until it has stopped growing. In continuous culture the fungus would continue growing all the time.

e This is a good answer, for both marks.

(b) The fungus is filtered off. The penicillin is then precipitated using calcium salts. It is then filtered off.

e This answer receives 4 marks. All that is missing is the **final drying**.

(c) (i) Rate = $(14 \, \mathrm{g} - 2 \, \mathrm{g})/40 \, \mathrm{h} = 0.3 \, \mathrm{g \, h^{-1}}$

e This receives 2 marks. The candidate has chosen the correct (straight line) region of the graph and performed the calculation correctly, but has omitted $\mathrm{dm^{-3}}$ from the final units, which should be $\mathrm{g \, dm^{-3} \, h^{-1}}$.

(ii) The carbohydrate source has been used up, so the fungus cannot grow any further without raw materials and energy.

e This is a good answer, for both marks.

Commercial biotechnology (II)

The diagram below shows the industrial plant used to produce high-fructose corn syrup which is used in some slimming foods. The three enzymes used in the process are immobilised in large columns.

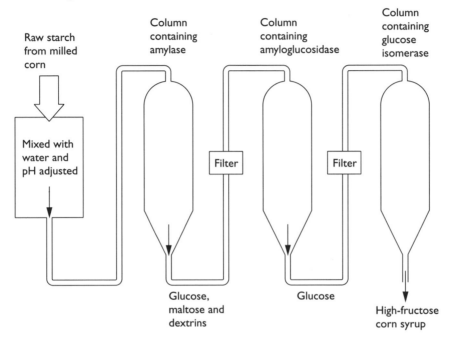

(a) Describe *two* methods of immobilising enzymes for a process such as this. (2 marks)

(b) Give the advantages and disadvantages of using immobilised enzymes, rather than microorganisms, in this process. (4 marks)

⑤ (c) Explain why the pH of the raw starch has to be adjusted. (2 marks)

⑤ (d) The temperature in the column containing amylase is maintained at 60 °C. Suggest an explanation for this choice of temperature. (4 marks)

Total: 12 marks

■ ■ ■

Answer to question 5: candidate A

(a) Cross-linking and entrapment

> ⓔ This receives 1 mark, for listing two methods. However, the question asks for descriptions, not a list.

(b) There is only one enzyme, so the product is purer. The concentration of the enzyme is higher than if whole microorganisms were used, so the reaction goes faster.

ℓ This receives 2 marks for advantages of immobilised enzymes over microorganisms. However, the question also asks for disadvantages.

(c) The enzyme has an optimum pH at which it works best.

ℓ This receives 1 mark for optimum pH. The second mark would have been awarded for an explanation of how pH affects enzyme structure.

(d) Enzymes work faster at higher temperatures — this must be the optimum temperature for amylase.

ℓ This receives 1 mark for optimum temperature, but there is no reference to the **energy of the particles** or to **denaturation** which **affects the enzyme's active site**.

■ ■ ■

Answer to question 5: candidate B

(a) The enzyme could be trapped inside alginate beads. It could also be adsorbed onto the surface of porous carbon.

ℓ This is a good answer, for full marks.

(b) An advantage is that the concentration of the enzyme is higher, so the reaction goes faster. A disadvantage is that pure enzymes are very expensive, so the running costs are higher.

ℓ This answer receives 2 marks out of 4. The question asks for advantages and disadvantages, and 4 marks are available, so more than one of each should have been given.

(c) pH affects the tertiary structure of enzymes, which are proteins. To obtain the maximum rate of reaction, the pH should be adjusted to the optimum for the enzyme. For most enzymes this is near pH 7.

ℓ This scores both marks.

(d) The higher the temperature, the higher is the rate of reaction, because the substrate particles have more energy and there are more successful collisions. However, above 37 °C, enzymes begin to denature, so a compromise temperature is used.

ℓ This receives 2 marks for the effect of temperature on reaction rate and 1 mark for denaturation. However, the candidate is under the misapprehension that all enzymes begin to denature at 37 °C; the amylase used here clearly denatures at a much higher temperature.

Question 6

Bacterial disease

(a) Describe *three* factors that affect the ability of bacteria to produce disease. (3 marks)

(b) Describe the symptoms of *Salmonella* food poisoning. (2 marks)

(c) There was an outbreak of food poisoning following a wedding reception. An investigation showed that cooked chicken had been left out in the kitchen for 4 hours before the meal. It also showed that one of the cooks was a carrier of the *Salmonella* bacterium. Suggest an explanation for the occurrence of the outbreak of food poisoning. (4 marks)

Total: 9 marks

Answer to question 6: candidate A

(a) Infectivity, invasiveness and whether it has a way of attaching itself to a host cell, for example by having a sticky capsule.

e This receives 2 marks, for stating three factors and describing one of them. Descriptions are lacking for infectivity and invasiveness.

(b) Sickness and diarrhoea

e This receives 1 mark for symptoms associated with the gut. There is no reference to **increased body temperature**.

(c) Perhaps the carrier did not wash his/her hands after going to the toilet. Germs might then have been transferred to the food.

e This receives 1 mark only. At A-level, there should be reference to **faeces** and to **bacteria** rather than 'going to the toilet' and 'germs'. There is no reference to the time of exposure of the chicken at room temperature.

Answer to question 6: candidate B

(a) Whether the bacterium has a method of attaching itself to a host cell, for example pili. Infectivity — the number of bacteria needed to cause the disease. The number is high for *Salmonella* food poisoning, but low for typhoid. Invasiveness — for example, whether the bacterium has the ability to enter the bloodstream by using enzymes to digest tissues.

e This is a complete answer, for full marks.

(b) Diarrhoea and a slight fever

e Both marks are awarded here for two different symptoms.

(c) Carriers pass bacteria in their faeces. These may then be passed onto the chicken if the cook does not wash his/her hands before preparing food. The bacteria will multiply rapidly at room temperature. The cooking temperature was not high enough to kill the bacteria.

> *e* This answer receives 3 marks. The final mark would have been obtained for stating that 4 hours at room temperature would result in enough bacteria to produce an infection.

uestion 7

Viral disease (I)

The diagram below shows the estimated number of deaths from AIDS in 2000.

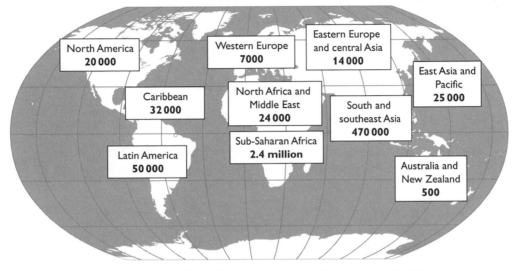

(a) Calculate the estimated number of people in western Europe who died from
   AIDS as a percentage of the estimated world total deaths from AIDS.   (2 marks)
(b) It is estimated that 2.4 million people died from AIDS in sub-Saharan Africa,
   compared with 20 000 in North America. Suggest an explanation for this.   (2 marks)
(c) Suggest *three* ways of reducing the incidence of AIDS in sub-Saharan Africa.   (3 marks)
(d) Describe the roles of DNA, mRNA and tRNA in the production of proteins for
   the HIV capsid in the cells of the host.   (4 marks)

Total: 11 marks

■ ■ ■

Answer to question 7: candidate A

(a) 0.029%

   e This scores nothing, since the answer is incorrect and no working is shown. If the
   correct working had been shown, the candidate would have received 1 mark for
   the method, despite making an arithmetic slip.

(b) AIDS is a sexually transmitted disease, so probably more people had unprotected
   sex in sub-Saharan Africa.

   e This receives 1 mark. There is no reference to **lack of education or finance for
   contraceptives and drugs.**

(c) Providing contraceptives; education; improving health care

   e These suggestions are all too vague to gain credit.

question

(d) The code on the viral RNA is copied to form mRNA, which then travels to the host ribosomes. Transfer RNA then makes the correct amino acids and mRNA joins them together to form a protein.

> This answer receives 3 marks. Transfer RNA does not synthesise amino acids; **different tRNA molecules bring specific amino acids to the ribosomes for assembly into proteins.**

Answer to question 7: candidate B

(a) 0.23391

> This answer receives both marks. However, an answer should not be given to so many decimal places. Always round off to the appropriate significant figures — in this case an appropriate answer would be 0.23.

(b) There is much more unprotected sex in sub-Saharan Africa. This might be because people are not educated about the dangers of infection.

> This is a good answer, for both marks.

(c) Educate people about the dangers of unprotected sex. Provide free contraceptives. Provide free drugs to HIV-positive people, so that they might not develop AIDS.

> This receives 2 marks. The final mark would have been gained by referring to **barrier** contraceptives or condoms.

(d) The viral DNA is translated into mRNA, which leaves the host nucleus and becomes attached to the ribosomes. Transfer RNA molecules then bring amino acids to the mRNA. The anticodons on the tRNA molecules line up with the codons on the mRNA molecules to ensure that the amino acids are in the correct order. The amino acids are then joined by peptide bonds.

> This is a good answer, for 3 marks. The candidate has confused translation with transcription. Transcription is copying the DNA code to mRNA. Translation is reading the mRNA code, to join amino acids in the correct sequence.

Q8 uestion

Viral disease (II)

(a) Describe the signs and symptoms of influenza. (3 marks)

(b) Describe the course of infection of influenza. (6 marks)

(c) Explain why elderly people need to be vaccinated against influenza every year. (3 marks)

Total: 12 marks

Answer to question 8: candidate A

(a) Sore throat, headache, fever

e This is enough for 3 marks.

(b) Influenza is an air-borne infection. It affects tissues in the throat. The virus bores its way into the host cell. Inside the host cell, new viruses are produced. When the host cells burst and release the viruses, they produce the symptoms of flu.

e This receives 2 marks, for air-borne infection and replication inside host cells. The answer lacks the detail needed for further marks. The virus does *not* bore its way into host cells.

(c) This is because their immune systems are weak.

e This answer receives 1 mark only, since the candidate has not referred to either virus or vaccine.

Answer to question 8: candidate B

(a) Aching joints, tiredness, headache

e This receives 2 marks. The symptoms given are correct, but **fever** is an important sign, which must be present for full marks.

(b) Influenza is a droplet infection. Tissues in the throat and bronchi may become infected. The whole virus enters the host cell by combining with the cell membrane. The viral RNA then separates from the capsid and enters the nucleus. Here the viral RNA is replicated. The viral RNA strands then enter the cytoplasm and join with proteins and lipids to form new viruses. The host cell then bursts, releasing viruses to infect more cells. At the same time, toxins are released from the host cell and it is these that cause the symptoms.

e This receives 5 marks. It lacks only reference to the role of viral RNA in the production of viral protein.

8
question

(c) The influenza virus has a high mutation rate. This means that memory cells produced as a result of previous vaccinations may not recognise new variants of the virus. The new vaccination stimulates production of memory B and T cells that recognise the new strain.

e This is a good answer, for full marks.

Question 9

Protection against disease (I)

Rubella is caused by a viral infection. The virus enters the body via the respiratory tract. The incubation period is about 18 days. The infection of the throat and larynx causes mild discomfort. A rash appears on the second day of the illness and disappears on the third day. Usually, the patient is clear of the disease after 6 days. The disease has disastrous effects on the fetus if a pregnant woman contracts it. It is recommended that all children are vaccinated against the disease.

(a) (i) How long after first being infected does the rubella rash appear?   (1 mark)
   (ii) Suggest what causes the rash.   (1 mark)
(b) Suggest when the person would be most infectious.   (1 mark)
(c) How does the body reduce the chance of viruses entering living cells in the
    respiratory tract?   (2 marks)
(d) Describe how the blood cells overcome the rubella infection.   (6 marks)
(e) Explain why a person who has recovered from rubella is immune to the disease
    for the rest of their life.   (3 marks)

Total: 14 marks

■ ■ ■

Answer to question 9: candidate A

(a) (i) 2 days

> *e* This scores nothing, since the candidate has not included the incubation period.

(ii) Toxins that are released by the virus.

> *e* This receives the mark for toxins, although the toxins are probably released when the host cells burst.

(b) During the time that the rash can be seen.

> *e* This receives the mark. The person is not infective during the incubation period.

(c) The virus is trapped by cilia on the surface of cells lining the trachea and bronchi.

> *e* This is a common error and scores no marks. Microorganisms are **trapped by mucus**, not by cilia. The cilia then move the virus out of the trachea.

(d) Some viruses are eaten by white blood cells. T-lymphocytes produce cytotoxins that kill viruses. B-lymphocytes produce antibodies that kill viruses and antitoxins that neutralise viral toxins.

> *e* This receives 3 marks for referring to cytotoxins, antibodies and antitoxins. At A-level, **phagocytosis** should not be referred to as 'eating'. There is no reference to **antigens** or to **cloning**.

(e) The antibodies that were produced in response to the attack remain in the body for a long time, waiting to attack the virus the next time it enters the body.

🖉 This misconception scores nothing. It is the **memory cells**, not the antibodies, which last for a long time.

Answer to question 9: candidate B

(a) (i) 20 days

🖉 Correct, for 1 mark.

(ii) Toxins released when the host cells burst.

🖉 This receives the mark.

(b) When the rash is visible.

🖉 Correct, for 1 mark.

(c) The virus is trapped by mucus lining the respiratory tract, and moved to the throat by cilia on the surface of cells. It can then be swallowed.

🖉 This is a complete answer, for full marks.

(d) T-lymphocytes recognise the antigens and clone to form killer T-cells, which produce cytotoxins that kill viruses. B-lymphocytes clone. The cloned cells produce antibodies that cause viruses to agglutinate. Antibodies also precipitate viral toxins and prevent viruses attaching to cell membranes.

🖉 This answer deserves 5 marks. The final mark would have been gained by reference to **phagocytosis**. There is one mistake — antibodies prevent bacteria, not viruses, attaching to cell membranes.

(e) After the first attack, memory B-cells remain in the body. They produce antibodies if the virus enters the body again.

🖉 This receives 2 marks. The final mark would have been gained by referring to rapid production of antibodies upon **re-infection**.

Q10

Question 10

Protection against disease (II)

Superbugs, which are highly resistant to antibiotics used by doctors, have been found in British farm animals. Livestock, particularly pigs, are a reservoir for powerful new bacteria that are a threat to human health.

Any humans infected through food or contaminated water with these bugs — new strains of *E. coli* and *Campylobacter* — are at serious risk because the bugs have become immune to the antibiotics that would normally be used to treat infection.

The problem has arisen through the massive use of antibiotics among animals on factory farms.

(a) (i) Describe the ways in which antibiotics affect bacterial cells.   (3 marks)

(ii) Give *two* ways in which bacteria resist the action of antibiotics.   (2 marks)

(b) (i) Describe how new strains of *Campylobacter* may have arisen.   (4 marks)

(ii) Explain why the proportion of resistant genes in the population may rise.   (3 marks)

Total: 12 marks

Answer to question 10: candidate A

(a) (i) They destroy bacterial cell walls and membranes. They also stop bacteria producing proteins.

e This receives 2 marks. Some antibiotics **prevent cell wall formation** rather than breaking down cell walls.

(ii) They produce enzymes that attack the antibiotics. They can also prevent antibiotics getting into the cells.

e This receives 1 mark for enzymes, but the second part of the answer is too vague to be awarded a mark.

(b) (i) By mutation. A mutation is a change in the DNA of the bacteria. This is brought about by deletion of amino acids.

e This receives 2 marks — for mutation and DNA. It is **bases** rather than amino acids which are deleted from DNA.

(ii) The non-resistant bacteria are killed by the antibiotic, but the resistant ones survive.

e This receives 1 mark for survival, but there is no reference to **reproduction** or **genes**.

Answer to question 10: candidate B

(a) (i) They prevent cell wall formation. They disrupt the functioning of the cell membrane. They interfere with synthesis of RNA.

e This is a good answer, for full marks.

(ii) They produce enzymes such as penicillinase which breaks down penicillin. Some have capsules which prevent antibiotics reaching the cell wall. The membranes become less permeable, preventing antibiotics getting in.

e This is a good answer, for both marks.

(b) (i) Mutation — changes in the base sequence of DNA.

e This receives 3 marks, for mutation and change in base sequence of DNA. The final mark would have been obtained by giving a method of changing base sequence, for example **deletion**.

(ii) The non-resistant bacteria are killed by the antibiotic. The resistant bacteria survive to reproduce. Therefore, their genes are passed on to the next generation, whereas the no-resistance genes are less likely to be passed on.

e This receives full marks.